SEARCH FOR SANTA

By
Anthony Tallarico

kidsbooks®
Incorporated

7004 N. California Ave.
Chicago, Ill. 60645

ISBN: 0-942025-71-7

Hardcover edition 1st published in 1990

Manufactured in the United States of America

Here we are at Santa's World Headquarters at the North Pole.

SEARCH FOR SANTA AT HIS HEADQUARTERS AND...

- ☐ Balls (3)
- ☐ Banana peel
- ☐ Candy canes (4)
- ☐ Dogs (2)
- ☐ Drummer
- ☐ Envelope
- ☐ Gingerbread house
- ☐ Goose
- ☐ Hammock
- ☐ Hearts (2)
- ☐ Igloo
- ☐ Jack-in-the-box
- ☐ Kite
- ☐ Lips
- ☐ Partridge in a pear tree
- ☐ Pick
- ☐ Pillow
- ☐ Rabbit
- ☐ Sandwich
- ☐ Skier
- ☐ Sleeping tree
- ☐ Sleigh
- ☐ Snowballs (3)
- ☐ Snow shovels (2)
- ☐ Snow women (2)
- ☐ Snowmen (2)
- ☐ Stars (4)
- ☐ Stocking
- ☐ Sunglasses
- ☐ Tepee
- ☐ Tricycle
- ☐ Wreaths (2)

BIKES
TRICYCLES
SLEIGH LOADING ZONE
?
IT WON'T FLY!
I LIKE IT!
I'M SANTA!
THANKS.
GINGERBREAD COOKIES HEADQUARTERS
COAL MINE
CANDLES
WRAPPING PAPER PLANT # 1
OOOPS!
HOME SWEET HOME
TREE ORNAMENTS
Z-Z-Z-Z!
PLUM PUDDING MAKERS
BOWS
?
DOLL FACTORY #7

Santa's elves work very hard to make sure the toys are ready by Christmas Eve.

SEARCH FOR SANTA IN THE ELVES' WORKSHOP AND...

- ☐ Baseball
- ☐ Boat
- ☐ Brushes (2)
- ☐ Coffeepot
- ☐ Crayons (2)
- ☐ Dogs (2)
- ☐ Ducks (2)
- ☐ Fire truck
- ☐ Football
- ☐ Hammers (2)
- ☐ Helicopter
- ☐ Kite
- ☐ Knife
- ☐ Mouse
- ☐ Paddle
- ☐ Piggy bank
- ☐ Pinocchio
- ☐ Robot
- ☐ Saw
- ☐ Scissors
- ☐ Screwdriver
- ☐ Star
- ☐ Teddy bear
- ☐ Telescope
- ☐ Toy soldier
- ☐ Train engines (4)
- ☐ Triangle
- ☐ Ventriloquist
- ☐ Yo-yo

JOE
MIKE
NINA
TONY
MAX
I LIKE IT!
I'M C-C-COLD!!
OOOPS!
HELLO!
THAT'S VERY GOOD!
MAMA!

Santa decided to do his Christmas shopping in town this year. He may never try this again!

SEARCH FOR SANTA IN TOWN AND...

- ☐ Bat
- ☐ Bird
- ☐ Candle
- ☐ Cats (2)
- ☐ Dog
- ☐ Drum
- ☐ Fishing pole
- ☐ Football
- ☐ Ice-cream cone
- ☐ Indian
- ☐ Paper airplane
- ☐ Pig
- ☐ Pizza
- ☐ Rabbit
- ☐ Radio
- ☐ Roller skates
- ☐ Scrooge
- ☐ Shark
- ☐ Ship
- ☐ Shovel
- ☐ Sled
- ☐ Snowmen (3)
- ☐ Star
- ☐ Stocking
- ☐ Sword
- ☐ Target
- ☐ Tepee
- ☐ Toast
- ☐ Train engine
- ☐ Turtle
- ☐ Wreaths (8)

HO-HO-YIPEEE!
HO-HO-OH, NO!
HO-HO-Z-Z-Z-Z-Z!
Ho-Ho-Ho!
Z
FOR RENT
HO-HO-HO!
HO-HO-HO!
HO-NO! GET ME OUT OF HERE!
HO-NO!!
COOL-YULE MOBILE
HO-HO-WOOF!
SANTA AT WORK
HO-HO-CHIRP!
HO-HO-HELP!
HO-HO-YUM!
HI, JOE!
DANGER STREET ICE
HO-HO-STUCK!
LA-
LA-
FA-
LA-
LA-
LA-
LA-
LA!
LA-
HO-HO-QUIET!
Ho-Ho-Ho!!

Santa's favorite story is *A Christmas Carol* by Charles Dickens.

SEARCH FOR SANTA IN "A CHRISTMAS CAROL" AND...

- ☐ Ball
- ☐ Bird
- ☐ Blue scarves (2)
- ☐ Bob Cratchit and Tiny Tim
- ☐ Broom
- ☐ Candle
- ☐ Christmas trees (2)
- ☐ Drum
- ☐ Elves (4)
- ☐ Fire
- ☐ Flowers
- ☐ Ghosts (4)
- ☐ Goose
- ☐ Jack-o'-lantern
- ☐ Ladder
- ☐ Lost hat
- ☐ Mailbox
- ☐ Muff
- ☐ Pie
- ☐ Scrooge
- ☐ Sherlock Holmes
- ☐ Sleds (2)
- ☐ Snowman-to-be
- ☐ Violin
- ☐ Wreath

SCROOGE and MARLEY
?
FASTER!
?
BULL'S-EYE!
BLESS US EVERY ONE!
WHERE IS BAKER STREET?
?
I..I'M SORRY!

Elves love to play baseball. Their rules are a little different, but they have just as much fun.

SEARCH FOR SANTA AT THE BASEBALL GAME AND...

- ☐ Apple
- ☐ Baseball
- ☐ Baseball caps (2)
- ☐ Bear
- ☐ Bowling ball
- ☐ Boxing gloves
- ☐ Cactus
- ☐ Candle
- ☐ Clown
- ☐ Elephant
- ☐ Fish (5)
- ☐ Fishing pole
- ☐ Flowers (2)
- ☐ Football
- ☐ Ice skates
- ☐ Igloo
- ☐ Lamp
- ☐ Mittens
- ☐ Mouse
- ☐ Octopus
- ☐ Pear
- ☐ Rabbit
- ☐ Rocking chair
- ☐ Seal
- ☐ Sled
- ☐ Stars (3)
- ☐ Sunglasses
- ☐ Target
- ☐ Top hats (2)
- ☐ TV set
- ☐ Umbrella
- ☐ Umpires (3)
- ☐ Wreath

I'M THE ABOMINABLE SNOWMAN! I PLAY THE ENTIRE OUTFIELD!
?
THIS GLOVE IS TOO BIG!
I'M THE UMP-IN-A-BOX!
I "BEAR-LY" UNDERSTAND THIS GAME.
UMP.
I'VE GOT IT....
I'M THE DESIGNATED SNOWBALL MAKER!
I WANT TO SCORE A BASKET!
WHICH WAY DO I RUN?
IS THIS AN ERROR?
DON'T ASK ME!
ICY ICE
?
IT'S ONLY 5 OUTS! I'M UP NEXT!
YUM... TASTY BAT!
WHAT'S THE SCORE?
THE SCORE IS 219 TO 184...AND THE GAME HASN'T EVEN STARTED!
I WANT A HOTDOG!
WHO'S ON FIRST?
WHO'S ON SECOND!

It's the morning of December 24th, and the elves are packing the sleigh. Can it take off with all that weight?

SEARCH FOR SANTA AT THE SLEIGH LOADING AND...

- ☐ Balloon
- ☐ Birdhouse
- ☐ Blimp
- ☐ Boat
- ☐ Camera
- ☐ Car
- ☐ Crayons (3)
- ☐ Flashlight
- ☐ Giraffe
- ☐ Guitar
- ☐ Hammer
- ☐ Hockey stick
- ☐ Horseshoe
- ☐ Kite
- ☐ License plate
- ☐ Mask
- ☐ Mechanic
- ☐ Needle
- ☐ Paintbrush
- ☐ Pencils (2)
- ☐ Pizza
- ☐ Rocking chair
- ☐ Sailboat
- ☐ Seal
- ☐ Skates
- ☐ Stockings (2)
- ☐ Tent
- ☐ Thread
- ☐ Train engine
- ☐ Tricycle
- ☐ Trucks (3)
- ☐ Windmill

OOOPS!
KEEP THEM COMING!
THIS ONE'S FOR MARY!
GRUNT!
THIS IS FOR A WEIGHT LIFTER!
GET ME A NEEDLE AND THREAD!
HOW ARE WE GOING TO PULL THAT LOAD?
I GIFT WRAPPED THIS!
I'M TIRED.
SANTA
I CAN FIX IT!

Christmas Eve. Time to deliver the presents. Wait—something is very wrong! The sleigh has taken off and Santa's not on it!

SEARCH FOR SANTA ON CHRISTMAS EVE AND...

- ☐ Balloons (2)
- ☐ Barrel
- ☐ Bird
- ☐ Blocks
- ☐ Candy canes (3)
- ☐ Chimneys (13)
- ☐ Dog
- ☐ Drum
- ☐ Eskimo
- ☐ Happy stars (2)
- ☐ Igloo
- ☐ Ladder
- ☐ Mrs. Claus
- ☐ Robot
- ☐ Sherlock Elf
- ☐ Snow woman
- ☐ Snowman
- ☐ Teddy bear
- ☐ Telephones (2)
- ☐ Telescopes (3)
- ☐ Tent
- ☐ Truck
- ☐ TV antennas (2)
- ☐ TV set
- ☐ Yo-yo

IT MUST BE CHRISTMAS EVE!
SANTA, WHERE ARE YOU?
I'LL JUMP ON WHEN IT PASSES!
SANTA'S NOT ON IT!
THE SLEIGH FEELS LIGHTER!
NO SANTA?
WE CAN'T GO WITHOUT HIM!
?
HAVE A GOOD TRIP!

Down the chimney he goes. But someone forgot to tell the family pet that Santa was coming!

SEARCH FOR SANTA AT HOUSE NUMBER 26 AND...

- ☐ Balloons (15)
- ☐ Bats (2)
- ☐ Bird
- ☐ Broom
- ☐ Burned out lights (6)
- ☐ Cactus
- ☐ Candles (2)
- ☐ Candy canes (3)
- ☐ Cat with a horn
- ☐ Cat in a hat
- ☐ Chairs (2)
- ☐ Christmas ornaments (4)
- ☐ Ducks (2)
- ☐ Elephant
- ☐ Fish
- ☐ Football
- ☐ Footprints
- ☐ Ghost
- ☐ Heart
- ☐ Jack-o'-lantern
- ☐ Kite
- ☐ Mitten
- ☐ Pencils (3)
- ☐ Mouse
- ☐ Pie
- ☐ Scarves (2)
- ☐ Stockings (3)
- ☐ Star
- ☐ Thermometer
- ☐ Traffic ticket
- ☐ Train engine
- ☐ Trash can
- ☐ Truck
- ☐ Trunks (2)
- ☐ Turtle
- ☐ Wreaths (4)

WHAT'S TAKING SANTA SO LONG?
HE'S PROBABLY EATING COOKIES!
HURRY UP, SANTA!
HE COULD BE ASLEEP!
THIS SLEIGH IS PARKED IN A SLEIGH NO PARKING ZONE!
NICE, DOGGY! SIT, DOGGY!
G-R-R-R-R!
FOR RENT
I'M PRACTICING FOR NEW YEAR'S EVE!
THIS IS MY SIZE!
I'M NOT YOUR SIZE!

That night Santa visits homes all over the world, bringing Christmas cheer to all!

SEARCH FOR SANTA DELIVERING PRESENTS AND...

- ☐ Airplane
- ☐ Arrows (3)
- ☐ Bat
- ☐ Book
- ☐ Burned out lights (6)
- ☐ Candles (2)
- ☐ Doll
- ☐ Drum
- ☐ Fake Santas (7)
- ☐ Football helmet
- ☐ Ghosts (2)
- ☐ Heart
- ☐ Ice-cream cone
- ☐ Kite
- ☐ Necktie
- ☐ Roller skate
- ☐ Scarf
- ☐ Sleigh
- ☐ Spotlight
- ☐ Stars (3)
- ☐ Teddy bear
- ☐ Thermometer
- ☐ Top hat
- ☐ Train engine
- ☐ TV antenna
- ☐ Wooden soldier
- ☐ Wreaths (10)

IT DOESN'T SNOW EVERYWHERE!
I'M NOT REAL!
I WISH I WAS REAL!
THANKS, SANTA!
I'M REAL!
MERRY CHRISTMAS! HO-HO-HO!
Z
THANKS, SANTA!
WELCOME SANTA
I'M NOT REAL!
I'M NOT REAL!
THANKS, SANTA!
THANK YOU, SANTA!
THANK YOU, SANTA!
THANKS, SANTA!
I'M NOT REAL!

Santa is homeward bound...or is he? Can he find his way back to the North Pole?

SEARCH FOR SANTA ON EARTH AND IN SPACE AND...

- ☐ Ballons (2)
- ☐ Banana peel
- ☐ Beam
- ☐ Cactus
- ☐ Camera
- ☐ Elephant head
- ☐ Eyeglasses
- ☐ Fish (3)
- ☐ Hamburger
- ☐ Hot dog
- ☐ Igloo
- ☐ Jet sleigh
- ☐ Kite
- ☐ Magnifying glass
- ☐ Movie star
- ☐ Paper airplane
- ☐ Periscope
- ☐ Pie
- ☐ Pizza
- ☐ Rabbit
- ☐ Sherlock Holmes
- ☐ Snowmen (2)
- ☐ Super hero
- ☐ Tall elves (2)
- ☐ Telescope
- ☐ Train engine
- ☐ Unicorn

WHERE IS SANTA?
HE'S GONE AGAIN!
WE TOOK OFF WITHOUT HIM!
SEARCH FOR SANTA!
SANTA IS A STAR!
NORTH POLE
I'M A REAL TREE!
I'M A MOVIE STAR!
I'M SANTA'S DOUBLE.
I'M SANTA'S TRIPLE.
?
?
?
THIS WILL BE MY GREATEST FILM!
"NORTH POLE SANTA AND THE TEMPLE OF TOYS!"
I SHOULD NEVER HAVE STOPPED HERE.
I THOUGHT ELVES WERE SHORT?!
WE CHANGED IT FOR THE FILM!
WE'LL MAKE YOU A STAR!
NOT IN THIS FILM!
I THOUGHT SANTA ONLY HAD REINDEER!

Home at last. Santa sure has a neat way of getting on and off his sleigh.

SEARCH FOR SANTA BACK AT THE NORTH POLE AND...

- ☐ Anteater
- ☐ Bats (2)
- ☐ Buffalo
- ☐ Camel
- ☐ Cheese
- ☐ Cow
- ☐ Dog
- ☐ Frog
- ☐ Flamingo
- ☐ Fox
- ☐ Kangaroo
- ☐ Kite (2)
- ☐ Ladder
- ☐ Mouse
- ☐ Owl
- ☐ Piggy bank
- ☐ Porpoise
- ☐ Rhinoceros
- ☐ Scarf
- ☐ Seal
- ☐ Star
- ☐ Toy soldier
- ☐ Umbrella
- ☐ Walruses (2)
- ☐ Wreath

?
WHO? SANTA THAT'S WHO!
I THOUGHT THIS WAS A GOOD WAY TO EXIT!
WHAT ARE YOU DOING UP HERE ??
I'M A BIG CHEESE!
WATCH OUT BELOW!
COME ON DOWN, SANTA!
I THINK I HEAR MY MASTER'S VOICE!
LOOK FOR SANTA!
HOLD ON SANTA, I'LL GET HELP!
I'M HUNGRY! HAS ANYONE SEEN ANY ANTS? YUM-YUM!
OINK!
I'M AN UNCLE!
NEXT TIME LET ME PULL THE SLEIGH!
HAS ANY-ONE SEEN CHEESE?

The elves have asked Santa to attend a meeting. He doesn't know why, but he soon gets quite a surprise!

SEARCH FOR SANTA AT THE SURPRISE PARTY AND...

- ☐ Balloon
- ☐ Bearded elf
- ☐ Clothesline
- ☐ Clown
- ☐ Cookies
- ☐ Elephant
- ☐ Envelope
- ☐ Fish
- ☐ Giraffe
- ☐ Hammer
- ☐ Heart
- ☐ Ice-cream cone
- ☐ Kiddie pool
- ☐ Mrs. Claus
- ☐ Reindeer
- ☐ Robot
- ☐ Saw
- ☐ Scooter
- ☐ Sir Prize
- ☐ Star
- ☐ Stocking
- ☐ TV camera
- ☐ Toy duck
- ☐ Wagon

WE'VE NEVER HAD A LESSON!
WE BELIEVE YOU!
ELVIS AND THE ELVES!
HAPPY BIRTHDAY, SANTA!
I LOVE LIVE MUSIC!
CAN I CUT IN?
I'M A COOKIE CREATURE!
MRS. CLAUS LIKES POPPING OUT OF A CAKE!
COOKIES! (ONLY AFTER YOU EAT YOUR DINNER!)
HOORAY FOR SANTA!!
THIS IS FOR SANTA.
I'M HUNGRY!

Santa goes to a warm place for vacation. It sure is a lot different than the North Pole!

SEARCH FOR SANTA AT SILLYGAN'S ISLAND RESORT AND...

- ☐ Bird
- ☐ Birdcage
- ☐ Clock
- ☐ Clothespin
- ☐ Dragon
- ☐ Duck
- ☐ Fire hydrant
- ☐ Fish tank
- ☐ Ghost
- ☐ Gravestone
- ☐ Hose
- ☐ King
- ☐ Lost hat
- ☐ Mermaid
- ☐ Monster
- ☐ Old tire
- ☐ Polluted water
- ☐ Rake
- ☐ Shark fin
- ☐ Skateboard
- ☐ Snakes (5)
- ☐ Snowman
- ☐ Starfish (3)
- ☐ Sunglasses (2)
- ☐ Surfer
- ☐ Table with 3 legs
- ☐ Volcano

HI, SANTA!
WE'RE ON VACATION TOO!
ARE YOU HAVING FUN?
WE ARE!
FOR SALE
I'M NOT GOING IN THAT WATER!
VERY VERY QUICK SAND
IT'S THE CREATURE!
NO! IT'S DAD! THE WATER IS POLLUTED!
I'D RATHER BE STUCK ON THIS ISLAND THAN SPEND MY VACATION THERE!
ME TOO!
SOMETHING IS FOLLOWING US!
I WISH THIS WERE A MOTORBOAT.
I WANT TO GO HOME!

It's time for Santa and the elves to start making lots of nice gifts for next Christmas.

SEARCH FOR SANTA AT THE WORKSHOP AND...

- ☐ Apple
- ☐ Bow
- ☐ Brush
- ☐ Car
- ☐ Drumstick
- ☐ Elves in trouble (3)
- ☐ Heart
- ☐ Iron
- ☐ Owl
- ☐ Pencil
- ☐ Scissors
- ☐ Screwdriver
- ☐ Triangle
- ☐ Truck

SEARCH FOR SANTA